THE GROSSEST BOOK OF WORLD RECORDS

THE GROSSEST BOOK OF WORLD RECORDS

Mel Cebulash

illustrated
by Steve Miller

Talisman Books Limited

Published by Talisman Books Ltd.,
18, Charing Cross Road, London WC2H 0HR, England.
First published by Pocket Books, New York, USA.

ISBN 0905983 246

First printed 1979
Second Printing 1981

Typesetting by Spectrum Typesetting Ltd, 227 Liverpool Road, London
Printed by Villiers Publications Ltd London NW5

Grossest Hall of Records

In 1978, plans were completed for the first permanent exhibit hall of gross memorabilia, and early in 1983 the hall will be opened to the public. Its site, the rear room of Lilly's Bar and Grill in Dean Street, London was selected from a list of thousands of applicants, and we believe it should attract millions of visitors annually.

At present, memorabilia collected for the permanent collection is being stored in a warehouse in Lower Marsh, London. The following description of items donated by record holders will probably send a chill up your spine. We certainly wish to extend our gratitude to the record holders, their families, and others for their generosity.

ARM (LENGTH)

DAVID "APE" SIMION OF LACEBY, LINCS., ENGLAND, HOLDS THE RECORD. ON MAY 14, 1978, DAVID'S RIGHT ARM MEASURED **164CMS** FROM ARMPIT TO FINGERTIPS. "YEARS AGO, I DISCOVERED THAT I COULD STRETCH MY ARM BY HANGING FROM THE GYMNASIUM BAR FOR AN HOUR **EVERY DAY,**" DAVID TOLD US. "I'M PLEASED TO HAVE THE RECORD, BUT I **WISH** I'D WORKED ON MY LEFT ARM, TOO." KEEP SWINGING DAVE!

ARMPIT ODOUR (GROUP)

THE **HONOURS** GO TO THE **PRENTISS** FAMILY OF SMETHICK, STAFFS., ENGLAND. A SLIGHT WHIFF OF **ANY** PRENTISS HAS BEEN CERTIFIED AS **HAZARDOUS** TO HUMANS. AN UNSUSPECTING POSTMAN ONCE SUFFERED TEMPORARY **PARALYSIS** FROM A WHIFF OF OLD MAN PRENTISS' ARMPIT. SINCE THEN, THE PRENTISS' POST HAS BEEN DELIVERED BY **CATAPULT**.

9

ARMPIT ODOUR (INDIVIDUAL)

WANDA FULLER OF MITCHUM, NEW MEXICO, HOLDS THE RECORD. AT ONE TIME OR ANOTHER, WANDA, 18, HAS SICKENED THE **ENTIRE** ADULT POPULATION OF MITCHUM, WHICH NUMBERS 3,702. WANDA RECENTLY COMPLETED HER HIGH SCHOOL DIPLOMA AT HOME AND HOPES TO GO **AWAY** TO COLLEGE. THEY WILL KNOW YOU ARE COMING WANDA.

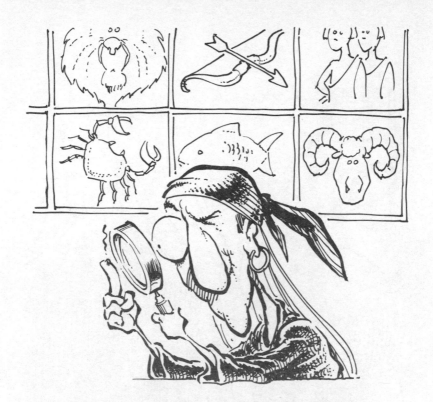

ASTROLOGICAL SIGN IDENTIFICATION (THROUGH EAR WAX)

DENISE LUCIANO OF MARGATE, KENT, ENGLAND HOLDS THE RECORD. ON NOVEMBER 17, 1977, DENISE CORRECTLY NAMED THE ASTROLOGICAL SIGNS OF **48 DIFFERENT PEOPLE** IN A ROW ON THE BASIS OF SAMPLES OF THEIR EAR WAX. "I CAN DO IT EVERY TIME," DENISE BOASTED TO US— "THAT IS, AS LONG AS I EXTRACT THE WAX. PISCES WAX IS THE **MOST DIFFICULT** TO ANALYSE, QUITE OFTEN IT LOOKS **VERY MUCH** LIKE VIRGO WAX."

BANDAGES (USED)

EMANUEL SORES OF SALAMANCA, SPAIN, HOLDS THE RECORD. AS OF APRIL 21, 1979, EMANUEL HAD 14,237 DIFFERENT **USED BANDAGES** IN HIS COLLECTION. "MORE THAN 5,000 OF THESE ARE **AUTOGRAPHED**," EMANUEL TOLD US, "AND THOSE PEOPLE WERE JUST **WONDERFUL**. A LOT OF THEM HAD PARTS OF THEIR BODIES **CUT OUT**, BUT THEIR HEARTS WERE AS BIG AS EVER."

BELLY-BUTTON LINT

BERGER WILLIAMS OF COTTONBALL, ARKANSAS, U.S.A., HOLDS THE RECORD. HE HAS FOUND LINT IN HIS BELLY BUTTON **EVERY NIGHT** SINCE JUNE 18, 1962. AN AMBITIOUS MAN, BERGER HAS CONVERTED THE LINT INTO FAME AND PROFIT FOR HIMSELF BY CREATING "PURE BELLY LINT" **HANDKERCHIEFS** FOR CELEBRITIES THROUGHOUT THE **WORLD**.

BODY HAIR
(FROM THE STARS)

RALPH ROBINSON OF LOS ANGELES, U.S.A.,
CLAIMED THE RECORD IN 1978. RALPH'S
COLLECTION INCLUDES **MOVIE, TV,** AND
SPORTS STARS. MANY OF THE HAIRS IN
RALPH'S COLLECTION HAVE COME FROM **DRAINS**
IN HOTEL BATHTUBS. "SOME STARS WILL JUST
GIVE YOU A BODY HAIR FOR YOUR
COLLECTION," RALPH NOTED, "BUT OTHERS ACT
AS IF YOU'RE **STRANGE.**"

BOGY   (LENGTH)

THE LONGEST CONTINUOUS BOGY EVER PULLED
FROM THE NOSE OF A HUMAN BEING WAS
PULLED ON JANUARY 27, 1973. AIDED BY A COLD,
CORA SIDON OF BIG SNEEZE, WYOMING, U.S.A.,
MANAGED TO EXTRACT A 62 CENTIMETRE BOGY
FROM HER **LEFT NOSTRIL**. CORA'S SECOND TRY
— FROM HER RIGHT NOSTRIL — STRETCHED TO
46 CENTIMETRES. UNFORTUNATELY, IT WAS
BROKEN BY AN AUTOGRAPH SEEKER WHO
PUSHED THROUGH THE CROWD OF DISGUSTED
ONLOOKERS.

BURPING

THE **LONGEST CONTINUOUS BURP** CAME FROM THE MOUTH OF **JOHN GASTON** ON JUNE 18, 1973. THE BURP LASTED FOR TWO MINUTES AND 38 SECONDS. THE BURP WAS TAPED AND LATER ISSUED AS A **45-RPM RECORD**. DURING NOVEMBER OF 1973, THE RECORD WAS ON THE **"TOP TEN" LIST. NOTE:** WHILE ATTEMPTING A **4-MINUTE BURP** DURING A PROFESSIONAL APPEARANCE IN ATLANTIC CITY, U.S.A., IN 1975, MR. GASTON PASSED OUT. TWO DAYS LATER, HE **DIED**.

CALLUS

IN A CONTEST HELD ON JULY 28, 1976, **ERNIE HOOFS** OF TULSA, U.S.A., PROVED THAT HE HAD DEVELOPED THE **THICKEST** LAYER OF FOOT CALLUS IN THE WORLD. IN THE FINAL EVENT OF THE DAY, ERNIE'S FOOT CALLUS WITHSTOOD A **.22 RIFLE BLAST**. A LIKE BLAST WENT RIGHT **THROUGH** THE FOOT OF ERNIE'S CLOSEST COMPETITOR.

CIGARETTE BUTTS

AFTER 40 YEARS, **MARY TOMPKINS** OF WOODY BAY, DEVON, ENGLAND HAS OVER TWO BILLION CIGARETTE BUTTS IN HER COLLECTION. THIS IS THE RECORD FOR THE **BIGGEST** COLLECTION. MARY ALSO HAS A SPECIAL COLLECTION OF **MOVIE STARS**' BUTTS. INCIDENTALLY, MARY DOESN'T SMOKE.

CRAWLING

PENNY PARKER, 19, OF KNEE DEEP, TEXAS, U.S.A., CRAWLED FROM SAN FRANCISCO TO NEW YORK. PENNY COVERED THE DISTANCE 3,415 MILES IN 82 DAYS DURING 1979. AT THE COMPLETION OF HER RECORD BREAKING FEAT, PENNY WAS UNABLE TO GET OUT OF HER CRAWLING POSITION AND HAD TO BE TAKEN HOME IN A PICKUP TRUCK.

DANDRUFF
(COLLECTION)

JOE GREEN OF SNOW HILL, LIVERPOOL,
ENGLAND HOLDS THE RECORD FOR THE
BIGGEST COLLECTION, AS OF MAY 19, 1979, JOE
HAD COLLECTED 80 KILOS OF DANDRUFF. HE
ALSO HAS A SPECIAL COLLECTION OF **EXTRA-
LARGE FLAKES**. WE THINK JOE STANDS **HEAD
AND SHOULDERS** ABOVE EVERYONE ELSE IN
DANDRUFF.

DEAD ANIMALS

GORDON YOUNGBLOOD, OF MOBILE, ALABAMA, U.S.A., HOLDS THE RECORD. SEVERAL YEARS AGO GORDON ACCIDENTALLY RAN OVER A **CAT**. SADDENED BY THE EVENT, HE SCOOPED UP THE CAT'S **DEAD BODY** AND TOOK IT HOME. AFTER THAT, HE BEGAN **COLLECTING** THE DEAD BODIES OF ANIMALS KILLED ON HIGHWAYS. HIS COLLECTION NUMBERS 1,327.

GORDON NOW LIVES WITH HIS COLLECTION IN A HOUSE TRAILER.

DIET (MOST UNUSUAL)

NATIVES OF THE SMALL ISLAND OF **POOCHANA** (NEAR NEW ZEALAND) HAVE THE MOST UNUSUAL DIET IN THE WORLD, IT CONSISTS SOLELY OF **EARTHWORMS**. "UNFORTUNATELY, OUR DIET WILL CHANGE," THE PRESIDENT OF POOCHANA TOLD US. "THE YOUNG PEOPLE ARE GETTING TIRED OF WORMS. A LOT OF THEM HAVE ALREADY STARTED EATING **BEETLES**."

DOG BITES

WINSTON TRAVERS OF ALPO, WEST VIRGINIA, U.S.A., HOLDS THE RECORD. BY THE END OF 1976, WINSTON HAD BEEN ON THE RECEIVING END OF **1,349 DOG BITES**. "THE FIRST FEW BITES WERE ACCIDENTS," WINSTON TOLD US, "BUT THEN I HIT UPON THE IDEA OF BEING ONE OF **THE GROSSEST**. I'M PROUD TO JOIN THE RANKS OF HUMAN ACHIEVERS."

DOG TEETH

ALICE HARPER OF AIRDALE, YORKS., ENGLAND, HOLDS THE RECORD. ALICE HAS 2,328 TEETH IN HER COLLECTION (AS OF 1979). "I HAVE AT LEAST ONE TOOTH FROM **EVERY** KNOWN BREED OF DOG," ALICE TOLD US. "WHEN I GET A DUPLICATE, I HAVE IT ADDED TO MY **CHARM BRACELET**. I THINK IT'S A VERY UNUSUAL BRACELET." IT SURE IS, ALICE!

DRAGGING
(BY HORSE)

DINAH O'ROUKE OF DINGLE, EIRE, HOLDS THE
RECORD. WITH HER LEFT **LEG** CAUGHT IN A
STIRRUP, DINAH WAS DRAGGED **SEVEN MILES**
BY HER PET HORSE, **FLICKA**. AFTER A SHORT
RECOVERY PERIOD AT THE LOCAL HOSPITAL,
DINAH CLAIMED THE DRAGGING RECORD. **NOTE**:
DINAH ALSO CLAIMED THE RECORD FOR
CREATING THE LONGEST CONTINUOUS **DITCH**,
BUT THIS HASN'T BEEN SUBSTANTIATED.

EARS (SIZE)

MARY McGEE OF ESGAIR, WALES HOLDS THE RECORD. EACH OF MARY'S EARS MEASURES **36CMS** FROM THE LOBE TO THE TOP OF THE EAR. MARY HAS WORKED AS A TELEPHONIST IN CARMARTHEN FOR SEVERAL YEARS, BUT SHE HOPES TO START HER OWN **ANSWERING SERVICE** SOON. "I PLAN TO CALL IT 'I'M ALL EARS'," MARY TOLD US.

EAR WAX (COLLECTION)

MARIKA FORTUNEV OF MOSCOW, U.S.S.R., HOLDS THE RECORD. SHE HAS **COLLECTED** EAR WAX FROM PERSONS FROM **EACH** OF THE MEMBER NATIONS OF THE **UNITED NATIONS** — WITH THE EXCEPTION OF THE SOVIET UNION. SO FAR, THE RUSSIANS HAVEN'T EXPLAINED THEIR REASONS FOR WITHHOLDING THE WAX.

EAR WAX (EATING)

ANDY GRIMES OF LOBE, MAINE, U.S.A., CLAIMS
THAT HE HAS EATEN HIS EAR WAX **EVERY DAY**
SINCE HE WAS SIX. MR. GRIMES, 101, CLAIMS IT
AS THE SOURCE OF HIS **GOOD HEALTH. NOTE**:
WE HAVE BEEN ABLE TO VERIFY 32 YEARS OF
EATING. THIS WAS SUFFICIENT FOR THE
RECORD. MR. GRIMES **ALSO** CLAIMED TO HAVE
EATEN HIS **WIFE'S** EAR WAX FOR 18 YEARS;
HOWEVER, BECAUSE SHE DIED IN 1951, THIS
CLAIM COULD NOT BE SUBSTANTIATED.

EGG SUCKING

HELENA ALBUMENTA OF HELSINKI, FINLAND, SET THE EGG-SUCKING RECORD ON MAY 15, 1979. HELENA SUCKED **43 EGG WHITES** THROUGH PINHOLES IN **ONE MINUTE**. WITH THIS AMAZING SUCKING FEAT, HELENA, 19, TOPPED HER OLD RECORD OF 37 EGGS IN ONE MINUTE. HELENA HOPES TO BE ABLE TO SUCK AN EGG A SECOND BEFORE SHE COMPLETES HER UNIVERSITY DEGREE IN GENETICS.

FAMILY (COLLECTION)

LEON PILDOW OF PEEBLES, SCOTLAND, HAS THE **LARGEST** FAMILY COLLECTION IN THE WORLD. SINCE 1854, **EVERY** PILDOW WHO HAS DIED HAS BEEN **STUFFED.** LEON'S COLLECTION, WHICH INCLUDES HIS GREAT-GREAT-GRANDMOTHER, NUMBERS 104 PILDOWS, "FOR A

WHILE, I HAD TO PUT THEM ALL IN **STORAGE**," LEON TOLD US, "BUT NOW I HAVE THEM ALL IN MY NEW 20-ROOM HOUSE. THEY'RE PART OF THE FURNISHINGS, YOU MIGHT SAY."

FEET (SMELL)

GEORGE DAVID, 18, HOLDS THE RECORD. ON
APRIL 21, 1978, GEORGE **TOOK OFF** HIS SHOES
AND WALKED THROUGH A **CROWDED** SHOPPING
CENTRE. IN THE 5 MINUTES HE HAD HIS SHOES
OFF, GEORGE MADE 29 PEOPLE **SICK** AND
CAUSED 12 OTHERS TO **PASS OUT**. AMBULANCE
MEN, WHO WERE ON STRIKE AT THE TIME,
CONSIDERED IT AN EMERGENCY AND LET THE
SICK THROUGH THE PICKET LINE.

FISH EYES

JONAH NEWTON OF MOUSEHOLE, CORNWALL, ENGLAND HOLDS THE RECORD. JONAH'S COLLECTION NUMBERS 22,178 FISH EYES (NOT ALL PAIRS). JONAH GOT HIS **FIRST** FISH EYE YEARS AGO FROM A SMOKED MACKEREL THAT HE PURCHASED AT A LOCAL FISH-MONGER. NOW HE'S TRYING TO KEEP HIS COLLECTION INTACT. "THERE ARE A LOT OF **ROBBERIES** IN THIS NEIGHBOURHOOD," JONAH TOLD US.

FLY WINGS (COLLECTION)

PENNY SYLVESTER OF STAGNANT FALLS, OREGON, U.S.A., HOLDS THE RECORD. AS OF AUGUST 13, 1979, PENNY HAD 1,119,578 FLY WINGS IN HER COLLECTION. "I **ACTUALLY** STARTED MY COLLECTION BACK IN **HOBOKEN, NEW JERSEY,**" PENNY TOLD US. "I HEARD SOME OTHER KIDS SAY THAT THEY WERE COLLECTING **'WINGS'**, SO I STARTED. LATER, I LEARNED THAT THEIR 'WINGS' WERE AIR FORCE PINS, BUT I **STAYED** WITH THE FLIES."

FUNERALS

EVE ANTHONY OF GRAVESEND, KENT, ENGLAND, HOLDS THE RECORD. EVE HAS ATTENDED 5,762 FUNERALS (SEPTEMBER 1979). EVE HOPES TO RAISE HER RECORD TO 10,000 BEFORE SHE RETIRES. "I WANTED TO BE ONE OF **THE GROSSEST,**" EVE TOLD US, "BUT I **NEVER** THOUGHT I WOULD MAKE IT." YOU MADE IT FINE, EVE!

GOING DIRTY

HARRY DIAL, 87, CLAIMS THE RECORD FOR
GOING WITHOUT **BATHING.** IN 1975, HARRY
SAID THAT HE HAD GONE 78 YEARS WITHOUT A
BATH. THIS CLAIM COULD NOT BE VERIFIED;
HOWEVER, THE MAN WHO OWNED THE BARN IN

WHICH HARRY LIVED VOUCHED FOR **40 YEARS,**
AND THIS WAS **ENOUGH** FOR THE RECORD.
NOTE: HARRY BROKE HIS NON-BATHING
STREAK IN 1975 WITH A WASH-UP IN THE
SAGAWAMBI RIVER. LOCAL OFFICIALS
IMMEDIATELY DECLARED THE RIVER
POLLUTED.

HAIR (GREASE)

HENRY SLICK OF GLENDALE, CALIFORNIA, U.S.A. HOLDS THE RECORD. ON DECEMBER 7, 1974, AN INDEPENDENT TESTING AGENCY CERTIFIED THAT HENRY'S HAIR CONTAINED **ENOUGH GREASE** TO LUBRICATE A MEDIUM-SIZED **CAR.** "I WANTED IT TO BE GREASY ENOUGH TO LUBRICATE A **TRUCK,**" HENRY TOLD US, "BUT I THINK I'M BEGINNING TO LOSE MY HAIR."

HAIR LICE

ANXIOUS TO BE INCLUDED IN THE GROSSEST, THE **ENTIRE** TOWN OF CRAWLING TOP, SOUTH DAKOTA, U.S.A., (POPULATION 3,129), PUT THEIR HEADS TOGETHER AND CAME UP WITH **HAIR LICE**. THEIR CLAIM THAT THE ENTIRE TOWN HAD HAIR LICE REACHED US ON SEPTEMBER 3, 1978. WE SENT A **BALD** INVESTIGATOR THERE, AND SHE VERIFIED THE CLAIM. GOOD WORK, CRAWLING TOP!

HAIR (UNWASHED)

ALVIN STEEN OF GREASLEY, NOTTS., ENGLAND HOLDS THE RECORD. ALVIN, A PUBLIC SCHOOL SPORTS MASTER, HAS NOT WASHED HIS HAIR IN 14 YEARS. "IT'S **GOOD LUCK**," ALVIN TOLD US. "I'VE HAD 14 WINNING SEASONS, BUT I GUESS I'M GOING TO HAVE TO WASH IT SOON. THE LOCAL PARSON RECENTLY SENT ME A BOOK TITLED, **PRAYING AT HOME WORKS**." BUT WILL IT WORK AS WELL AS YOUR HAIR ALVIN?

I.Q. AND AGE DIVINATION (THROUGH VOMIT)

HORACE EINSTEIN OF BOSTON, U.S.A., IS THE WORLD'S GREATEST VOMIT ANALYZER. IN INDEPENDENT TESTS PERFORMED AT A **MAJOR** UNIVERSITY IN THE BOSTON AREA, HORACE HAS NEVER FAILED (IN 142 TESTS) TO GIVE THE **AGE AND I.Q.** OF A PERSON AFTER ANALYZING A SMALL SAMPLE OF FRESH **PUKE** FROM SAID PERSON. "I WILL SOON BE ABLE TO NAME THE PERSON'S **SEX,** TOO," HORACE TOLD US. WE HOPE SEX DOESN'T RUIN HORACE!

LEFTOVERS FROM THE STARS

NICK PALLEY OF NEW YORK CITY HOLDS THE RECORD. NICK GETS HIS LEFTOVERS FROM RESTAURANTS. HIS COLLECTION OF LEFTOVER FOOD (WHICH HE SEALS IN PLASTIC) NUMBERS 1,143 SEPARATE LEFTOVERS FROM THE PLATES OF SOME OF THE MOST FAMOUS PEOPLE IN THE WORLD. "I **BUY** THE LEFTOVERS," NICK TOLD US, "BUT I HAVE TO BE CAREFUL. A LOT OF WAITERS TRY TO SLIP ME **ORDINARY** LEFTOVERS. IF A STAR DIDN'T LEAVE IT, I DON'T WANT IT."

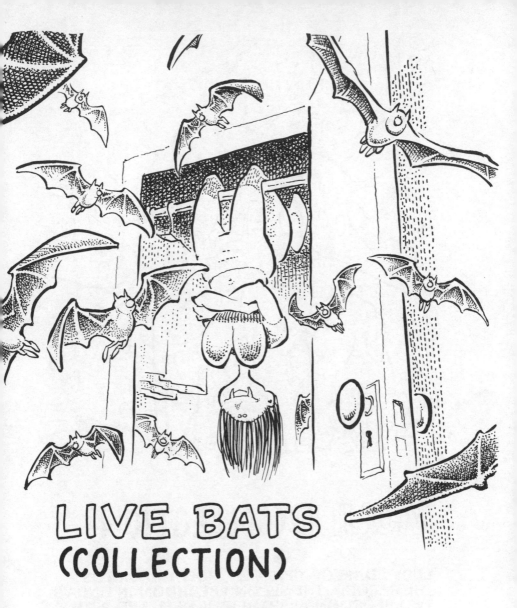

LIVE BATS
(COLLECTION)

EVA FLINCH OF VAMPDORF, W. GERMANY,
HOLDS THE RECORD. EVA HAD 143 BATS IN HER
THREE-ROOM APARTMENT IN 1977. EVA CLAIMS
MOST OF THEM ARE **HOUSEBROKEN**, THOUGH
WE DIDN'T STAY AROUND LONG ENOUGH TO
VERIFY HER CLAIM. "IT'LL BE GOOD TO BE
GROSS," EVA TOLD US. " THE PEOPLE AROUND
HERE THINK I'M **BATTY**." OH, NO EVA — YOU'RE
GROSS!

MOULD (COLLECTION)

LUCY EDAM OF TIP-TOPEN, HOLLAND, HOLDS THE RECORD. THE SECOND BEDROOM IN LINDA'S TWO-BEDROOM APARTMENT WAS **FILLED** WITH MOULD WHEN WE CHECKED ON AUGUST 14, 1979. "I STARTED WITH A FEW STALE PIECES OF **BREAD**," LUCY INFORMED US. "ACTUALLY, THE RECORD WON'T LAST. **ANYONE** WITH A BIG HOUSE AND A DESIRE TO BE ONE OF THE GROSSEST CAN PROBABLY **TOP** MY COLLECTION."

MOTH AND BUTTERFLY (EATING)

LINDA PLEISTER, OF GROSS GAP, INDIANA, U.S.A., HOLDS THE RECORD. OF THE 140,000 SPECIES OF MOTHS AND BUTTERFLIES IN THE WORLD, LINDA HAS **TASTED** 39,542 (OCTOBER 1979). OF THESE, 38,170 HAVE BEEN MOTHS. "I'VE NEVER REALLY GOTTEN USED TO EATING **BUTTERFLIES,**" LINDA TOLD US.

MOUTH
(BAD BREATH)

"GARLIC" JEAN PIERRE RIEK, 19, HOLDS THE RECORD. ON JUNE 14, 1978, JEAN PIERRE ENTERED A CROWDED LIFT IN BOUSIGUE, FRANCE. BY THE TIME THE LIFT REACHED THE 11th FLOOR, EIGHT PEOPLE WERE **RETCHING** IN AGONY, TWO HAD **PASSED OUT,** AND ONE MAN'S MUSTACHE HAD TURNED GREY. JEAN PIERRE'S GIRL FRIEND RECENTLY HAD HER NOSE REMOVED SURGICALLY.

MUSCLES (ARM)

JOHN SHEPARD, 19, HAS THE WORLD'S LARGEST
BICEP. CONCENTRATING ALL OF HIS EFFORTS
ON HIS RIGHT ARM, JOHN DEVELOPED A RIGHT
BICEP THAT MEASURES 82cm FLEXED (1978).
JOHN WEIGHS ONLY 44 KILOS, AND DOCTORS
WHO HAVE EXAMINED HIM ESTIMATE THAT HIS
RIGHT ARM CONSTITUTES ALMOST **HALF** HIS
WEIGHT. KEEP LIFTING, JOHN!

MUSCLES (CALF)

PATRICIA ATLAS, 17, HAS THE WORLD'S LARGEST CALF, WHICH SHE DEVELOPED BY CONCENTRATING ON A LEG WEAKENED BY A CHILDHOOD ILLNESS. PATRICIA'S LEFT CALF MEASURES 75cm FLEXED (1979). WHEN ONE CONSIDERS THAT PATRICIA'S LEFT **THIGH** MEASURES ONLY 48cm, ONE REALIZES HOW REMARKABLY GROSS SHE IS!

MUSCLES (CHEST)

SEYMOUR BREST OF PULLOVER, AUSTRALIA, HAS THE WORLD's LARGEST CHEST. SEYMOUR'S CHEST MEASURES 221 cms EXPANDED, THOUGH HIS **WAIST** MEASURES ONLY 82 cm (1978 MEASUREMENTS). **NOTE:** THIS RECORD IS FOR MUSCULAR CHEST. SEVERAL **FAT SLOBS** WHO CLAIMED THE TITLE HAVE BEEN DISQUALIFIED. SEYMOUR'S RECORD IS ALL THE MORE IMPRESSIVE WHEN ONE CONSIDERS THAT HIS **RIGHT PECTORAL** NEVER RESPONDED TO EXERCISE.

MUSCLES (NECK)

HORACE VORSTER OF BIG SHIRT, SOUTH AFRICA, HAS THE WORLD'S **MOST MUSCULAR** NECK. HORACE'S NECK MEASURED 65cms IN 1979, AND HIS TOTAL BODY WEIGHT AS ONLY 152 POUNDS. "BEFORE I STARTED EXERCISING," HORACE TOLD US, "I HAD A **PUNY** NECK. WELL, IT'S NOT PUNY NOW." IT SURE ISN'T, HORACE!

NOSE-BLOWING (TAPINGS)

BOB ZENTER OF HILLSIDE, NEW JERSEY, U.S.A. HOLDS THE RECORD. DURING 1978, BOB HAD CAPTURED ON TAPE 3,956 DIFFERENT PEOPLE **IN THE ACT** OF BLOWING THEIR NOSES. "I SUPPOSE YOU COULD SAY THAT I ENJOY HEARING PEOPLE BLOW THEIR NOSES," BOB EXPLAINED TO US. "THAT'S NOT COMPLETELY TRUE, BUT SOME DO HAVE REAL **STYLE**." SO DO YOU, BOB!

NOSTRIL HAIR (FULL GROWTH)

RUSS ROBINSON OF HURRACAINE, WEST KIRBY, ENGLAND, IS THE UNDISPUTED RECORD-HOLDER. HE SPORTS A **FULL HANDLEBAR MUSTACHE** MADE OF NOSTRIL HAIR. SURPRISINGLY ENOUGH, RUSS HAS BEEN **BALD** SINCE CHILDHOOD.

NOSTRIL HAIR
(SINGLE STRAND)

AT THIS WRITING, **LILLIAN PRELL** OF
HAMPSTEAD, LONDON, ENGLAND, HAD A 125cm
HAIR GROWING OUT OF HER RIGHT **NOSTRIL**.
THIS IS THE RECORD FOR A **SINGLE STRAND** OF
NOSTRIL HAIR. THE HAIR IS STILL GROWING, AND
LILLIAN HOPES TO SEE IT REACH 200cm. THEN
SHE PLANS TO CLIP IT AND **AUCTION** IT OFF,
WITH THE PROCEEDS GOING TO **CHARITY**. WE
HOPE YOU MAKE IT, LILLIAN!

PEANUTS (EATING)

HARDLY CARTER OF ATLANTA, U.S.A., HOLDS THE RECORD. ON SEPTEMBER 15, 1979, HE ATE 14,752 PEANUTS — **WITH** THEIR SHELLS — IN NINE HOURS. CARTER COULD VERY WELL HAVE CONSUMED **MORE** PEANUTS DURING THE NINE HOURS, BUT HIS PERFORMANCE WAS **INTERRUPTED** BY 15 MINUTES OF **CHOKING** ON A SHELL.

PHOTO COLLECTION (MOST UNUSUAL)

AKIRA YASHIKA OF FUJI, JAPAN, IS OUR CHOICE FOR THE RECORD. AS OF 1979, AKIRA'S COLLECTION OF **OPEN-COFFIN FUNERAL PICTURES** NUMBERED 11,459. "I SNAP A FEW HUNDRED EACH YEAR," AKIRA TOLD US, "BUT THE BULK OF MY COLLECTION CAME THROUGH THE MAIL. PEOPLE HAVE EVEN STARTED NAMING ME IN THEIR WILLS SO THAT I'LL RECEIVE OPEN-COFFIN PHOTOS OF THEM. I GUESS THEY'RE SEEKING **IMMORTALITY**."

PIGS (LIVING WITH)

ON A BET, **KENNY LUCAS** OF SLIGO, EIRE, MOVED INTO A **PIG PEN** ON JUNE 1, 1975. THREE MONTHS LATER (OCTOBER 1), HE CRAWLED OUT

OF THE PEN WITH THE **WORLD'S RECORD** FOR A
HUMAN LIVING WITH PIGS. "DURING THE DAY
THEY'RE ALL RIGHT," KEN TOLD US, "BUT I DON'T
THINK I COULD EVER GET USED TO THEIR
SNORING."

RAW LIVER
(EATING)

KATHERINE GUTMAN, OF CRAWLEY, ENGLAND, HOLDS THE RECORD. ON JANUARY 14, 1975, KATHERINE ATE FOUR KILOS OF **RAW CHICKEN LIVERS** IN 12 MINUTES. IN ACQUIRING THIS HUMAN RECORD FOR CONSUMPTION OF RAW LIVER, KATHERINE ALSO TOPPED THE **ANIMAL** RECORD OF THREE KILOS HELD BY A FOX TRAINED BY PETER PERDUE.

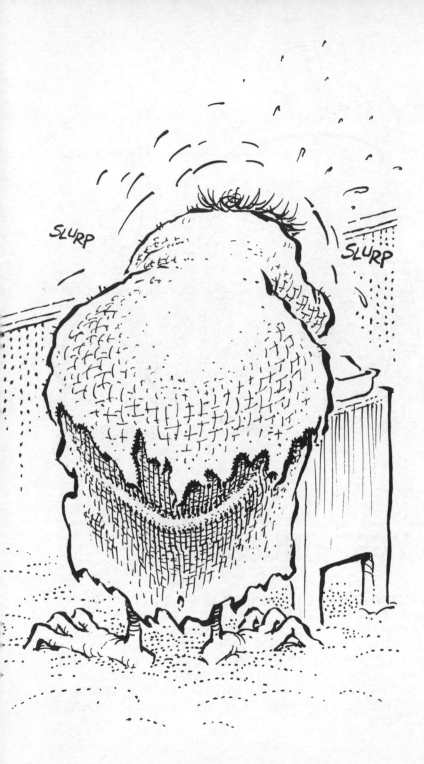

RESTAURANT
(MOST UNUSUAL)

TOM McCANN OF DENVER, U.S.A., IS OUR PICK FOR THIS RECORD. TOM'S SHOES INN RESTAURANT HAS LEATHER WALLS, LEATHER CHAIRS, AND LEATHER TABLE TOPS, AND **ALL** OF THE LEATHER COMES FROM DISCARDED **SHOES**. "I'M CLOSED DURING THE SUMMER," TOM TOLD US. "THE PLACE SMELLS LIKE A FOOT IN WARM WEATHER." TOO BAD, TOM, BUT IT'S STILL **QUITE A FEAT**!

RINGWORM
(LARGEST)

ON DECEMBER 14, 1979, DOCTORS IN HOUSTON, TEXAS, CERTIFIED THAT 99 PERCENT OF **KAREN MONROE'S** BODY WAS COVERED WITH RINGWORM. THIS TOPS THE **OLD** RECORD OF 94 PERCENT RINGWORM SET BY **GEORGE "DUSTY" CRUEX** IN 1942 AT THE U.S. ARMY INDUCTION CENTRE IN NEW YORK CITY. BY THE WAY, CRUEX WAS **INVALIDED OUT**.

RUNNING NOSE

SHEILA SIMON OF HOT SPRING, SOUTH AFRICA, HOLDS THE RECORD. HER NOSE HAS RUN **CONTINUOUSLY** SINCE MAY 1, 1971. IN ADDITION, SHE ALSO CLAIMS THE RECORD FOR THE USE OF **TISSUES**. "I'VE USED OVER A MILLION TISSUES," SHE SNIFFED. **NOTE:** WE WERE UNABLE TO VERIFY HER TISSUE CLAIMS.

SCABS (COLLECTING)

RANDY JONES OF DOESKIN, AUSTRALIA, HOLDS
THE RECORD. RANDY HAS BEEN COLLECTING
SCABS SINCE HE WAS 8 YEARS OLD. HE
ESTIMATES THAT HE HAS OVER **2,000 SCABS** IN
HIS COLLECTION, AND IT IS STILL GROWING. IN
AN AVERAGE WEEK, RANDY RECEIVES ABOUT 40
SCABS IN THE POST FROM FANS, BUT HE OFTEN
REJECTS SMALL ONES. "I'M AS PICKY AS EVER,"
HE SAYS.

SCABS (EATING)

THE **POKEDIS TRIBE** FROM THE SMALL ISLAND
OF BLEEKMON IN THE PACIFIC THRIVES ON
SCABS. THE PRACTICE OF EATING SCABS,
WHICH HAS BEEN CARRIED ON FOR SEVERAL
GENERATIONS, IS TIGHTLY **CONTROLLED** ON
BLEEKMON, AND THE **ENTIRE POPULATION**
TURNS OUT EACH YEAR FOR THE ANNUAL SCAB
BAKE.

SNAKE-BITE SUCKING

BEN SAWYER OF FANGS, MEXICO, HAS BEEN
SUCKING SNAKE BITES FOR **OVER** HALF A
CENTURY, FOR THE FIRST 30 YEARS, BEN, 84,
KEPT NO RECORDS, BUT SINCE THEN, HE HAS
REGISTERED 143 SNAKE-BITE SUCKINGS, FOR
THE WORLD'S RECORD. IN ALL HIS YEARS OF
SUCKING, BEN HAS **NEVER** SUFFERED AN ILL
EFFECT, "THE STUFF TASTES TERRIBLE THOUGH,"
BEN TOLD US.

SNEEZING

DOLLY PATCHIN OF ALLERGY FALLS, AUSTRALIA HOLDS THE RECORD. SHE HAS BEEN SNEEZING **EVERY 30 SECONDS** SINCE AUGUST 24, 1947. AT THIS WRITING, HER SNEEZES NUMBER IN THE **MILLIONS** AND SHE WAS STILL GOING STRONG! AND YOU SHOULD SEE HER EAT — **GROSS, REALLY GROSS!**

SPIT (COLLECTION)

DURING 1978, THE **TOWNSPEOPLE** OF ACHTEN, EAST GERMANY, SET THE RECORD. IN A LITTLE LESS THAN A YEAR, THEY MANAGED TO COLLECT **OVER 400 LITRES** OF SPIT IN A TANK DONATED BY THE CHAMBER OF COMMERCE. "A FEW **POOR SPORTS** REFUSED TO CONTRIBUTE," ACHTEN'S MAYOR TOLD US, "BUT THE GOOD CITIZENS WANTED THE RECORD, AND WE'RE **PROUD** OF IT."

SPORTS (BOGY FLICKING--MOVING TARGET)

SCORING WITH 5 BOGIES, **CARL VINCENT**, 16, BECAME THE BOGY-FLICKING CHAMPION (MOVING TARGET) OF THE WORLD. THE COMPETITION, HELD ON EASTER SUNDAY, 1979, WAS MARRED BY THE **DISQUALIFICATION** OF A PLAYER WHO WAS FOUND TO HAVE A **NOSTRIL FULL** OF BOGIES SUPPLIED BY FRIENDS.

SPORTS (BOGY FLICKING--STATIONARY TARGET)

VERONICA SHELTON OF MINNEAPOLIS, U.S.A., HOLDS THE RECORD. VERONICA SCORED **SEVEN BULL'S-EYES** FLICKING AT AN APPROVED TARGET IN THE ONE MINUTE ALLOTED TO COMPETITORS. VERONICA SET HER RECORD ON OCTOBER 23, 1977. VERONICA PROBABLY WOULD HAVE SCORED **MORE** BULL'S-EYES HAD SHE NOT RUN OUT OF BOGIES WITH 15 SECONDS REMAINING.

SPORTS (CATCHING FRISBEE BETWEEN TEETH)

ON JUNE 3, 1978, **MILKA PROVESKI** OF ODESSA U.S.S.R., SET THE RECORD. IN ONE HOUR, MILKA MANAGED TO CATCH 342 FRISBEES OUT OF 1,000 TOSSED BETWEEN HER TEETH. MILKA MIGHT HAVE DONE BETTER, BUT SHE WAS HAMPERED BY A **BROKEN NOSE** SUSTAINED WHEN SHE **MISJUDGED** A TOSS EARLY IN THE HOUR.

SPORTS (LIFTING LITRE CONTAINERS OF MILK)

ARNOLD WEIDMAN OF YORK, ENGLAND, HOLDS THE RECORD. USING HIS RIGHT ARM, ARNOLD RAISED A LITRE CONTAINER OF MILK OVER HIS HEAD **52,485 TIMES** ON FEBRUARY 14, 1979. "I REALLY WANTED TO DO IT 60,000 TIMES," ARNOLD TOLD US, "BUT I'M PLEASED AND PLAN TO GO AFTER THE FIVE LITRE CONTAINER RECORD".

SPORTS
(LIFTING WITH PIERCED EAR)

MARIE FEMYASHA OF THE SOVIET UNION
HOLDS THE RECORD. ON OCTOBER 13, 1972,
MARIE MANAGED TO RAISE A 42-KILO WEIGHT
THAT HAD BEEN ATTACHED TO A **SPECIAL
EARRING** HOOKED ONTO HER LEFT EAR LOBE.
"I'M PLEASED TO HAVE THE RECORD," MARIE
TOLD US, "BUT I DON'T THINK IT'S **GROSS**."

SPORTS
(LIVE-MAGGOT EATING)

IRA NEFF OF RESTON, VIRGINIA, U.S.A., HOLDS
THE WORLD'S RECORD. IN THE FIRST ANNUAL
LIVE-MAGGOT EATING CONTEST (JULY 4, 1979)
HELD IN HOBOKEN, NEW JERSEY, IRA MANAGED
TO DOWN SEVEN LIVE MAGGOTS. "I COULDN'T
REALLY **TRAIN** FOR THIS," IRA TOLD US, "BUT I
PROMISED MYSELF TO DO THE BEST I COULD. I'M
GLAD I WON, BUT IT WOULD HAVE BEEN MORE
OF AN HONOUR IF **SOMEONE ELSE** HAD
ENTERED." BETTER LUCK NEXT TIME, IRA!

SPORTS
(SEWER SWIMMING)

ON JULY 20, 1975, A TEAM OF FOUR SWIMMERS
REPRESENTING **ANN ARBOR**, MICHIGAN, U.S.A.,
SET A **NEW** RECORD FOR THE EIGHT-MILE
COURSE SET UP IN NEW YORK CITY'S SEWER
SYSTEM. SWIMMING **AGAINST** THE TIDE, THE
ANN ARBOR TEAM COVERED THE COURSE IN SIX
HOURS AND 15 MINUTES. LATER, AFTER A
HOSING BY FIREMEN, EACH MEMBER OF THE
TEAM WAS AWARDED A GOLD **SEWER PLATE**.

SPORTS
(SPITTING--MOVING TARGET)

SCORING WITH A **DIRECT HIT** ON THE DRIVER OF A MOTORCYCLE PASSING AT 90 M.P.H., **WALTER YERKES**, 26, CAPTURED THE WORLD'S SPITTING CHAMPIONSHIP (MOVING TARGET) FOR 1979. "I ACTUALLY OWE THIS TITLE TO MY **FRIENDS**," WALTER TOLD US. "I'VE BEEN SPITTING AT THEM FOR **MONTHS**, TRAINING FOR THIS EVENT."

SPORTS
(TOOTHPASTE EATING)

ESTHER PARKER OF GLEEM, HAMPSHIRE, ENGLAND SET THE SPEED RECORD ON JULY 14, 1977. IN LESS THAN SIX SECONDS, ESTHER **SQUEEZED** A FAMILY-SIZE TUBE OF TOOTHPASTE DOWN HER THROAT. HER CLOSEST COMPETITOR **GAGGED** ON HALF A TUBE, AND IT TOOK HER MORE THAN 6 SECONDS TO DO IT, TOO. **NOTE**: ESTHER WAS **JAILED** IN 1974 FOR EATING TOOTHPASTE IN A GLEEM SUPERMARKET. "I COULDN'T AFFORD TOOTHPASTE ANYMORE," ESTHER TOLD THE COURT, "AND I HAD TO STAY IN SHAPE".

TEETH (CAVITIES)

ALVIN STEINER OF SUGARTOP, PENNSYLVANIA, U.S.A., HOLDS THE RECORD FOR THE **MOST** CAVITIES FOUND IN A **SINGLE** CHECKUP. ON NOVEMBER 21, 1978, SEVERAL DENTISTS CHECKED ALVIN'S MOUTH. THEY NOTED 64 CAVITIES. THIS TOTAL TOPS THE OLD RECORD OF 53 (ALSO HELD BY STEINER). SMILING WITH HIS 13 REMAINING TEETH, STEINER SAID THAT HE **HOPED** TO HAVE 80 CAVITIES BY 1980.

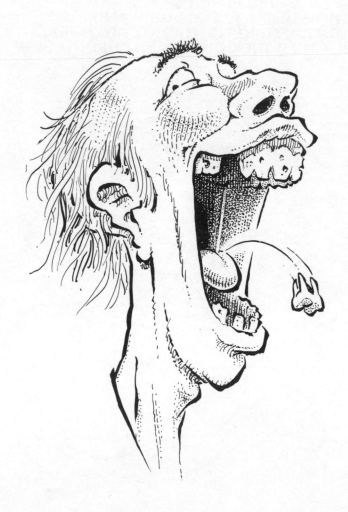

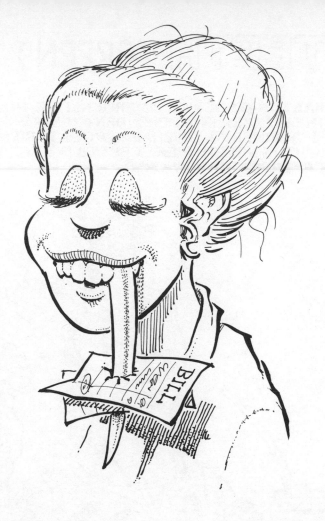

TEETH (EYETOOTH)

THE **LONGEST** EYETOOTH EVER FOUND IN A HUMAN MOUTH BELONGS TO **CAROLINE GUMMER** OF COLGATE, DENMARK. CAROLINE'S LEFT EYETOOTH MEASURES 18 CENTIMETRES FROM THE GUM TO THE POINTED END OF THE TOOTH. DENTISTS WHO CHECKED CAROLINE'S TOOTH TO **VERIFY** THIS RECORD SAY THAT IT IS **STILL** GROWING, CAROLINE IS 17.

TEETH (GREEN)

BARTON O'SHEA OF LIMEROCK, EIRE, HOLDS THE RECORD. IN INDEPENDENT TESTS PERFORMED AT SEVERAL **LABORATORIES**, BARTON'S TEETH WERE CERTIFIED TO BE THE **GREENEST** IN THE WORLD.

TOBACCO (CHEWING)

CHARLES WICK, 91, OF DURHAM, IOWA, U.S.A., HOLDS THE RECORD. HE HAS BEEN CHEWING SINCE HE WAS SIX. HE ESTIMATES THAT HE HAS CHEWED OVER **FIVE TONS** OF TOBACCO DURING HIS LIFE-TIME. AFTER SPRAYING SOME JUICE THROUGH HIS **BLACK TEETH,** CHARLES TOLD US, "ACTUALLY, I PREFER **GUM,** BUT I WAS ALWAYS WORRIED ABOUT CAVITIES."

TOE JAM
(COLLECTION)

JEFF SCHOLL OF SMUCKER, ZIMBABWE-
RHODESIA, HOLDS THE RECORD. THROUGH 1979.
JEFF HAD **FOUR LITRE JARS** FULL OF HIS OWN
TOE JAM. "I STICK WITH MY OWN," JEFF TOLD US.
"AFTER A LONG RUN ON A **HOT DAY**, I CAN
SCRAPE NEARLY AN **OUNCE** OF IT FROM
BETWEEN MY TOES."

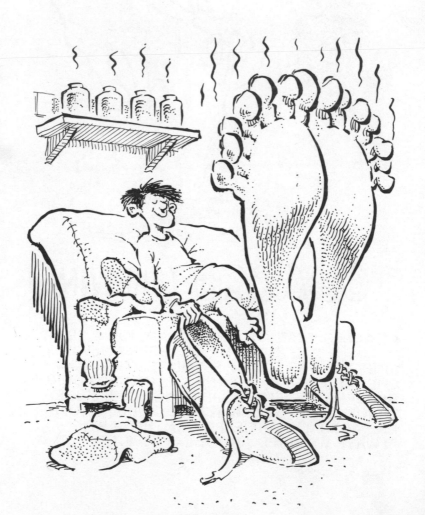

TOENAILS

SUSAN DEMPSTER OF BIG FOOT, NEW ZEALAND, HAS THE LARGEST COLLECTION OF TOENAILS IN THE WORLD. AT THIS WRITING, HER COLLECTION NUMBERS IN THE **THOUSANDS,** AND SHE IS ASSURED OF NINE NEW NAILS A WEEK (FROM HERSELF). SUSAN ACCIDENTLY **CLIPPED OFF** ONE OF HER TOES SEVERAL YEARS AGO.

TOILET-PAPER TUBES (COLLECTION)

VICTORIA SCHABINSKY OF CRAKNAU, POLAND, HOLDS THE RECORD. VICTORIA'S TOILET-PAPER TUBE COLLECTION NUMBERED 1,436,328 TUBES IN 1975. VICTORIA STARTED HER COLLECTION IN 1949, BUT SINCE THEN FRIENDS, NEIGHBOURS, AND EVEN **STRANGERS** HAVE ADDED TUBES. "CAN YOU IMAGINE HOW **PROUD** I AM TO GET SUCH RECOGNITION?" VICTORIA ASKED US. WE COULDN'T IMAGINE, BUT WE ASSURED VICTORIA THAT IT WOULD BE A LONG TIME BEFORE HER RECORD WAS **WIPED OUT!**

TRAVELLING
(INSIDE GARBAGE TRUCK)

AIDED BY **THOUSANDS** OF MUNICIPAL WORKERS, **RAYMOND SWILL** OF JERSEY CITY, NEW JERSEY, TRAVELLED FROM NEW YORK TO CALIFORNIA INSIDE **GARBAGE TRUCKS.** THE ENTIRE TRIP TOOK HIM 28 DAYS (JUNE 2-30, 1978). **NOTE:** AT TRANSFER POINTS, RAYMOND WAS ALLOWED **ONE-MINUTE RESTS** BEFORE BEING DUMPED INTO NEW GARBAGE.

UNCOOKED SPAGHETTI

KITTY KELLY, 16, OF LISBURN, NORTHERN IRELAND, HOLDS THE RECORD. ON APRIL 11, 1979, KITTY ATE 9.5 KILOS OF **UNCOOKED SPAGHETTI** IN A LITTLE UNDER 2 HOURS. IN CRUNCHING HER WAY TO THE RECORD, KITTY DEFEATED **SEVEN** OTHER CONTESTANTS.

UNDERARM HAIR (COLLECTION)

EVITA SEGOVIA OF AVILA, SPAIN, HOLDS THE RECORD. AS OF FEBRUARY, 9, 1977, EVITA HAD SAMPLES OF UNDERARM HAIR FROM 11,432 PEOPLE. **"MOST** OF IT IS BROWN,"** EVITA TOLD US, "THOUGH IT'S HARD TO TELL BROWN FROM BLACK. OH, I HAVE SOME FROM **STARS**, BUT I WOULD JUST AS SOON GET IT FROM **ORDINARY** PEOPLE. I'M JUST AN ORDINARY PERSON." YOU WERE, EVITA, BUT NOW YOU'RE ONE OF THE **GROSSEST!**

USED CHEWING GUM

THE ENTIRE STUDENT BODY OF **NEW END SCHOOL,** HAMPSTEAD, ENGLAND, HOLDS THE RECORD. DURING THE 1977 SCHOOL YEAR, THE STUDENTS SAVED **ALL** THEIR USED CHEWING GUM. THE RESULTING BALL OF USED GUM WEIGHED **314 KILOS.** LATER, IT WAS SOLD TO AN UNNAMED GUM **RECYCLING PLANT.**

USED SOAP

BILL BUBBLES, A TRAVELLING SALESMAN FROM JACKSON, MISSISSIPPI, U.S.A., HOLDS THE RECORD. BILL HAS OVER 3,000 PIECES OF USED SOAP IN HIS COLLECTION, AND THE PIECES COME FROM **MOTELS** IN EACH OF THE 50 STATES AND THE DISTRICT OF COLUMBIA. WORKERS AT THE MOTELS SAVE THE USED SOAP FOR BILL. "**THEY** THOUGHT I WAS **GROSS** LONG BEFORE I HEARD OF YOUR BOOK," BILL TOLD US.

WARDROBE
(MOST UNUSUAL)

AGNES VAN DUKE OF ELDEN, HOLLAND, HAS
THE WORLD'S MOST UNUSUAL WARDROBE. ALL
OF HER CLOTHING IS MADE OF **SNAKE SKINS.** "I
LOVE THE FEEL OF SNAKE," AGNES TOLD US,
"THOUGH I MUST SAY THAT I STILL FIND THE
UNDERTHINGS A LITTLE **SLIMEY.**"

WARTS (PERSONAL)

ON JANUARY 18, 1973, WE CHECKED **SUSAN HOPPER** OF FROGTOWN, AUSTRALIA. WE FOUND THAT HER BODY HAD 173 WARTS ON IT. THIS TOPS THE OLD RECORD OF 143 HELD BY **LISA WRIGHT** OF MUDDYPAW, ILLINOIS, U.S.A. AS FAR AS WE CAN GUESS, **NO ONE** WILL COME CLOSE TO SUSAN.

Memorabilia Donated
and held in the
Grossest Collection

ARM (Length) — David "Ape" Simion provided an X ray of his right arm. Actually, two pictures were necessary to get David's entire right arm.

BELLY BUTTON LINT — Berger Williams provided a banner of "pure belly lint" for the exhibit hall.

BOGY (Length) — Cora Sidon's mother provided the first booger pulled from Cora's nose. It measures 12 centimetres and is sealed in plastic.

BURPING — A tape of John Gaston's last burp was provided by radio station WHAG in Atlantic City.

CALLUS — Ernie Hoofs provided a piece of callus chipped from his foot by a laser beam.

DANDRUFF (Collection) — Joe Green provided three ounces of unidentified dandruff.

DIET (Most Unusual) — The people of Poochana provided an autographed photo of their president officiating at the annual earthworm harvest.

DOG TEETH — Alice Harper donated a charm bracelet of poodle teeth.

EAR WAX (Collection) — Marika Fortunev provided a sample of ear wax from Mali.

EGG SUCKING — Helena Albumenza provided 43 hollow eggs.

FAMILY (Collection) — Leon Pildow provided his great grand-uncle Mortimer Pildow.

FISH EYES — Jonah Newtown provided a pair of eyes from a butterfish.

GOING DIRTY — Local officials provided a quart bottle of water from the polluted Sagawambi River.

HAIR (Unwashed) — Alvin Steen personally delivered a lock of his hair after it was refused by postal authorities.

LEFTOVERS FROM THE STARS — Nick Palley provided a half-eaten corn on the cob, which he states "was left by Don Rickles in Nathan's on Forty-third and Broadway in New York City on July 25, 1948."

NOSE-BLOWING (Tapings) — Bob Zenter provided a three-minute tape titled "Members of Congress Blow Their Noses — Guess Who?"

PEANUTS (Eating) — Hardly Carter donated an autographed copy of his book, *Peanuts Can Change Your Life.*

PIGS (Living With) — Kenny Lucas provided "the only pair of underpants I wore when I set my record. They haven't, as you might guess, been washed."

RINGWORM (Largest) — George "Dusty" Cruex sent a picture of himself snapped in 1942. "Although my record has been broken," George wrote, "I'm proud that I held it for thirty years and I wish Karen the same good luck." (*Note:* George starred in the 1955 motion picture *The Monster Who Walked the Earth*).

RUNNING NOSE — Sheila Simon provided an autographed tissue.

SCABS (Collecting) — Randy Jones provided a 400 gram scab. "I believe this is the heaviest scab in the world," Randy wrote. "It fell off a rhino."

SNEEZING — Dolly Patchin provided a copy of her hit L.P. album entitled "Rocking with Dolly and the Gesundheits."

SPORTS (Barefoot Waterbug Crunching) — Larry Leech provided a short movie of his record-breaking run.

SPORTS (Catching Frisbee Between Teeth) — Milka Proveski provided the frisbee that broke her nose the day she set her record.

TEETH (Cavities) — Alvin Steiner provided an X ray of his mouth taken at the National Institute of Dental Disease.

TEETH (Green) — Barton O'Shea provided a color photo of his teeth. (*Note:* The photo was being used for color matches by a company that manufactures astro-turf.)

TOBACCO (Chewing) — Charles Wick provided a chewed plug of his "favourite tobacco."

TOE JAM (Collection) — Jeff Scholl provided a 56 gram jar of "Jeff Scholl's Peach State Toe Jam."

USED CHEWING GUM — The alumni of New End School provided a 50 kilo ball of used sugar-free gum.

WARTS (Personal) — Susan Hopper sent an autographed photo of her bare back.